YO-AET-206

Working with 3-digit Numbers

Module Structure

Comparison of two numbers	S1–S6
Forming the greatest and the smallest numbers	S7–S8
Ordering numbers	S9–S10
Skip counting	A1, S11–S13
Rounding off numbers	S14–S16
Practice problems	S17

Learning Outcomes

By the end of this module, the student will be able to:

- Compare and order two numbers
- Form the greatest and the smallest numbers
- Skip count by 2, 3, 5, 10 and 100
- Round off 3-digit numbers

Date: [ ]   Status: [ ]

1 Write the two numbers and compare them.

(a)

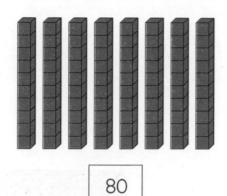   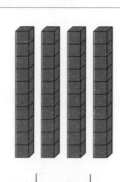

80   40

Which of the two is greater? 80

(b)

   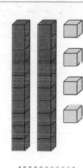

[ ]   [ ]

Which of the two is greater? [ ]

(c)

   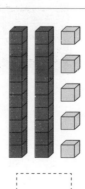

[ ]   [ ]

Which of the two is greater? [ ]

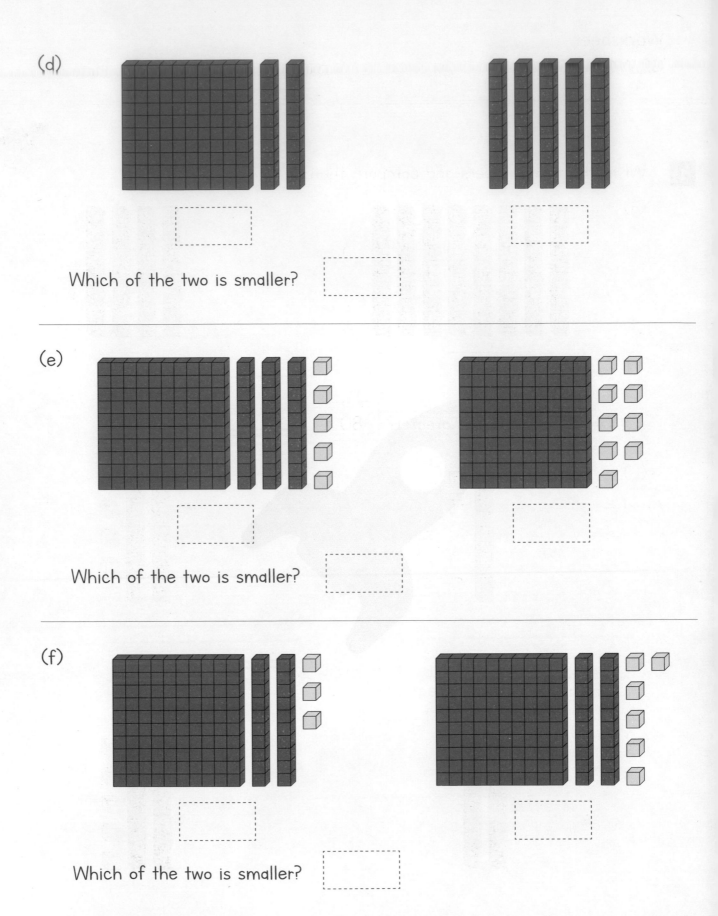

(d)

[ ] [ ]

Which of the two is smaller? [ ]

(e)

[ ] [ ]

Which of the two is smaller? [ ]

(f)

[ ] [ ]

Which of the two is smaller? [ ]

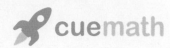

1 Write the two numbers and compare them.

(a)

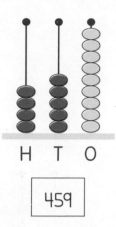

H T O

459

H T O

721

721 is greater than 459 .

(b)

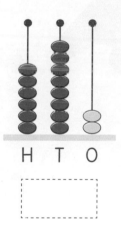

H T O

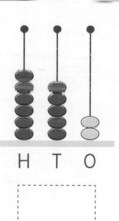

H T O

is greater than .

(c)

H T O

_____

H T O

_____

_____ is greater than _____ .

(d)

H T O

_____

H T O

_____

_____ is smaller than _____ .

(e)

H T O

_____

H T O

_____

_____ is smaller than _____ .

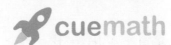

1 Compare the two numbers. Use >, <, or =. Also write the comparison statement.

(a)

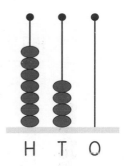

H   T   O

>

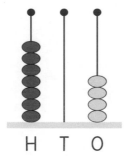

H   T   O

740 > 704

(b)

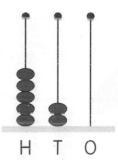

H   T   O

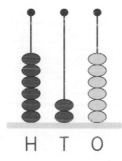

H   T   O

(c)

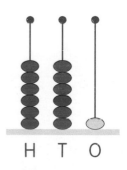

H   T   O

H   T   O

2   Write the two numbers and compare them. Use >, <, or =.

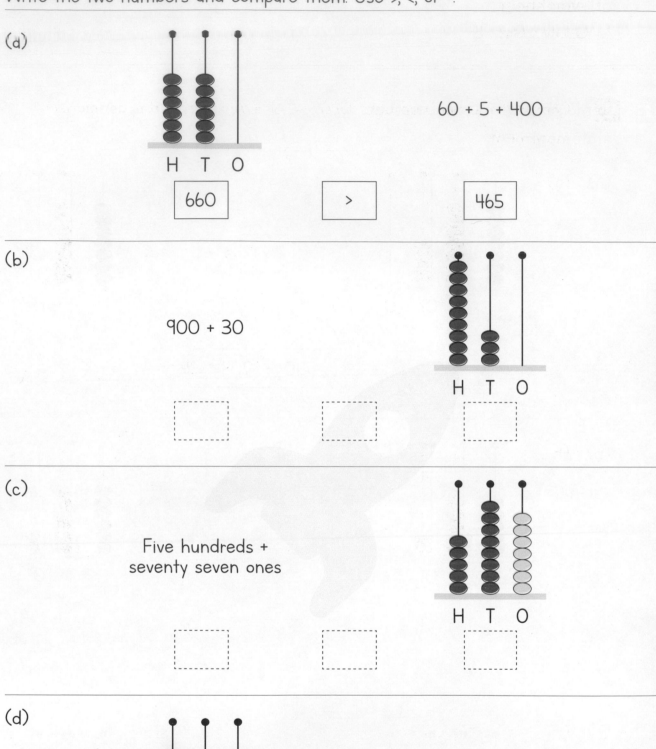

(d)

H T O

60 + 5 + 400

| 660 | > | 465 |

(b)

900 + 30

H T O

☐   ☐   ☐

(c)

Five hundreds +
seventy seven ones

H T O

☐   ☐   ☐

(d)

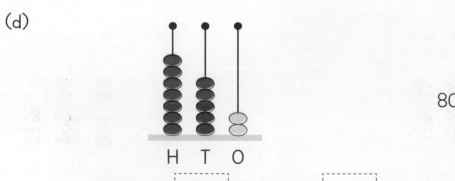

H T O

800 + 50 + 2

☐   ☐   ☐

Date:

Status:

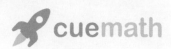

1 Write the comparison statement for the boxed numbers.

(a)

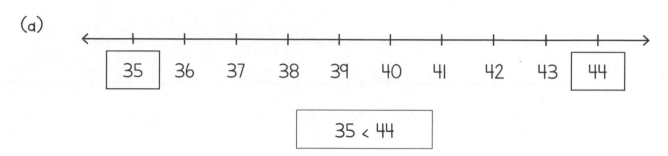

35 < 44

(b)

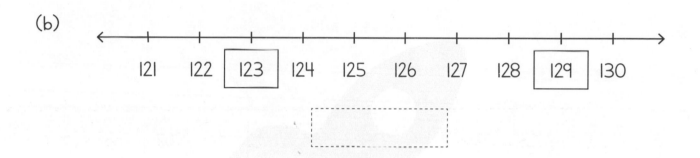

(c)

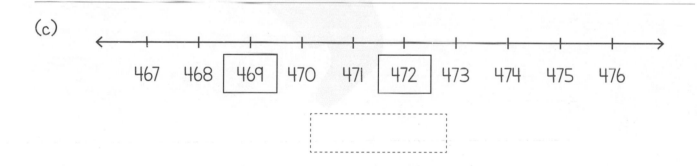

(d)

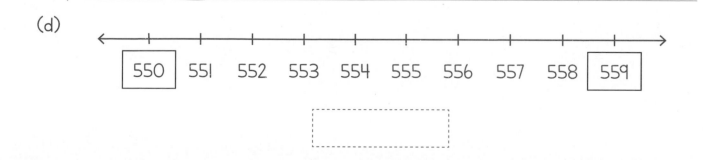

(e)

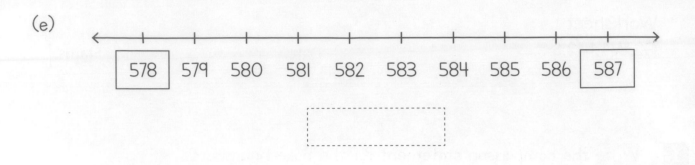

(f)

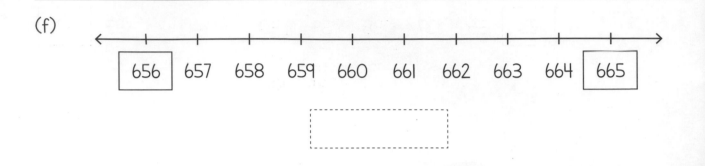

(g)

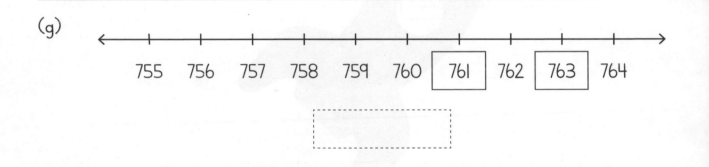

(h)

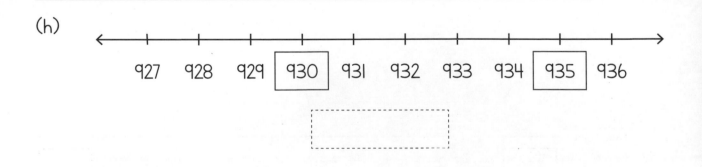

Date: [ ]   Status: [ ]

1 Compare the two numbers. Use >, <, or =.

(a) 310 | < | 314

(e) 820 [ ] 820

(b) 675 [ ] 576

(f) 239 [ ] 238

(c) 409 [ ] 409

(g) 362 [ ] 762

(d) 576 [ ] 576

(h) 297 [ ] 927

2 Compare the two numbers. Use >, <, or =.

(a) One hundred twenty four | > | One hundred twelve

(b) Three hundred eighty [ ] Three hundred eighty

(c) Seven hundred seventeen [ ] Seven hundred seventy

(d) Four hundred forty five [ ] Fifty five

(e) Nine hundred sixty three [ ] Six hundred ninety three

(f) Eight hundred eight [ ] Eight hundred eight

(g) Eight hundred nine [ ] Eight hundred nineteen

3 Answer the following questions.

(a) Mala has 3 hundred-rupee notes, 4 one-rupee coins, and 8 ten-rupee notes. Jaya has 8 one-rupee coins, 3 hundred-rupee notes, and 4 ten-rupee notes. Who has more money?

Mala has:
3 hundred-rupee notes =
$$3 \times 100 = ₹300$$
8 ten-rupee notes = $8 \times 10 = ₹80$
4 one-rupee coins = $4 \times 1 = ₹4$
Total = ₹384

Jaya has:
3 hundred-rupee notes =
$$3 \times 100 = ₹300$$
4 ten-rupee notes = $4 \times 10 = ₹40$
8 one-rupee coins = $8 \times 1 = ₹8$
Total = ₹348

$$₹384 > ₹348$$

Mala

(b) Prithvi and Priya went to a shop. Prithvi bought a pair of shoes for 6 ten-rupee notes, 2 one-rupee coins, and 5 hundred-rupee notes. Priya bought a jacket for **six hundred twenty five** rupees. Who spent less money and how much was spent?

[ ] [ ]

(c) Vinu's store sells a Hot Wheel's toy car for **three hundred twenty eight** rupees. Ben's store sells the same kind of toy car for ₹382. Write the smaller amount.

₹ [ ]

12

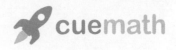

1 Answer the following questions.

(a) Suma picked up 105 shells at the beach on a Saturday and **one hundred fifty** shells on a Sunday. On which day did she pick up more shells?

[   ]

(b) Kavya's school has 795 students and Om's school has 975 students. Whose school has less students?

[   ]

(c) India scored 301 runs in a match and Sri Lanka scored **one hundred thirty** runs in the same match. Who scored more runs?

[   ]

(d) There are **two hundred thirty** trees in Deer Park and 320 trees in Flower Park. Which park has less trees?

[   ]

2 Write the expanded form of each number. Then write the greatest and the smallest numbers.

(a) 640,   528,   732

640 = | 600 + 40 |

528 = | 500 + 20 + 8 |

732 = | 700 + 30 + 2 |

Greatest:

Smallest:

(b) 528,   258,   825

528 =

258 =

825 =

Greatest:

Smallest:

(c) 482,   488,   842

482 =

488 =

842 =

Greatest:

Smallest:

Date: [ ]   Status: [ ]

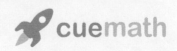

1 Write the expanded form of each number. Then write the greatest and the smallest numbers.

(a) 521,   251,   215

521 = [ ]

251 = [ ]   Greatest: [ ]

215 = [ ]   Smallest: [ ]

(b) 977,   979,   997

977 = [ ]

979 = [ ]   Greatest: [ ]

997 = [ ]   Smallest: [ ]

2 Circle the greatest number.

(a)	413,	(632,)	432	(d)	718,	645,	555
(b)	746,	466,	647	(e)	521,	522,	520
(c)	209,	920,	290	(f)	624,	426,	642

3   Circle the smallest number.

(a)	291,	219,	(209)	(d)	663,	790,	366
(b)	115,	515,	151	(e)	988,	898,	889
(c)	376,	637,	763	(f)	743,	373,	337

4   Make the smallest possible 3-digit number and the largest possible 3-digit number using all the three digits given.

	Digits	Smallest possible number	Largest possible number
(a)	3, 2, 4	234	432
(b)	8, 6, 3		
(c)	7, 9, 1		
(d)	1, 4, 0		
(e)	8, 9, 0		

Date: [ ]   Status: [ ]

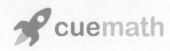

1 Answer the following questions.

(a) Roy paid ₹395 for a teddy bear, **five hundred thirty nine** rupees for a toy bus, and ₹935 for a doll. For which item did he pay the most (the greatest number)?

[ ]

(b) A bakery baked the following number of biscuits.

Day	Monday	Tuesday	Wednesday
Biscuits	676	766	667

On which day did the bakery bake the least biscuits (the smallest number)?

[ ]

(c) Ravi thinks of a number greater than 285 and less than 300. It has the digit 4 in it. What is the number?   [ ]

Anil thinks of a number greater than 479 and less than 529. It has the digits 7 and 1 in it. What is the number?   [ ]

Priya thinks of a number greater than 970 and less than 995. It has two 8s in it. What is the number?   [ ]

Who thought of the greatest number?   [ ]

Answer the following questions.

(a) Which is the largest 3-digit number?

(b) Which is the greatest 3-digit number with no 9s?

(c) Which is the smallest 3-digit number with no 0 or 1?

(d) Which is the smallest 3-digit number that can be made with 5, 3, and 7 with one digit repeated twice?

(e) Which is the largest 3-digit number that can be made with 9, 2, and 4 with one digit repeated twice?

(f) Which is the smallest 3-digit number that can be formed using any three digits out of 2, 1, 0, and 7 without repeating any of them?

(g) Which is the greatest 3-digit number with only 3 and 5?

(h) Which is the smallest 3-digit number that has only one 3 in it and does not have a 0, 1, or 2?

Date: [   ]   Status: [   ]

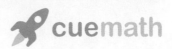

1 Arrange the numbers in ascending (increasing) order.

(a) 565,   560,   558,   567

| 558 | < | 560 | < | 565 | < | 567 |

(b) 392,   387,   394,   389

[   ] < [   ] < [   ] < [   ]

(c) 484,   479,   488,   482

[   ] < [   ] < [   ] < [   ]

(d) 805,   796,   802,   799

[   ] < [   ] < [   ] < [   ]

(e) 898,   907,   900,   910

[   ] < [   ] < [   ] < [   ]

2 Mark the numbers on the number line.

(a) A = 730,   B = 737,   C = 732,   D = 735

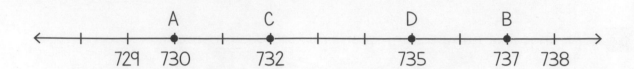

(b) A = 369,   B = 375,   C = 368,   D = 378

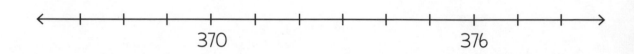

(c) A = 481,   B = 487,   C = 485,   D = 480

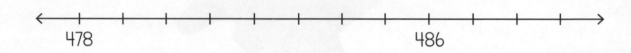

(d) A = 625,   B = 626,   C = 618,   D = 620

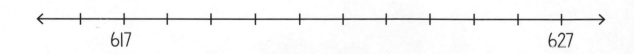

(e) A = 855,   B = 858,   C = 851,   D = 850

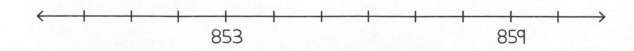

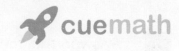

Date: [   ]   Status: [   ]

---

1   Do as directed.

(a) Make four 3-digit numbers with the digits 7, 2, and 4 without repeating any of them. Then arrange the numbers in descending order.

Numbers: | 247 | 427 | 742 | 274 |

Descending order:

| 742 | > | 427 | > | 274 | > | 247 |

(b) Make four 3-digit numbers with the digits 5, 1, and 8 without repeating any of them. Then arrange the numbers in descending order.

Numbers:

Descending order:

(c) Make four 3-digit numbers with the digits 9, 0, and 6 without repeating any of them. Then arrange the numbers in ascending order.

Numbers:

Ascending order:

2 Answer the following questions.

(a) The time taken to screen four movies is given.

Dhoom: 129 min
Robot: 185 min
Lagaan: 225 min
Swades: 210 min

Arrange the numbers in decreasing order.

```
┌─────────────────────────────────────────────────────────┐
│                                                         │
│                                                         │
└─────────────────────────────────────────────────────────┘
```

(b) The number of stamps collected by four friends is given.

Sam: 445
Rig: 545
Yash: 454
Dev: 554

Arrange the number of stamps collected in increasing order.

```
┌─────────────────────────────────────────────────────────┐
│                                                         │
│                                                         │
└─────────────────────────────────────────────────────────┘
```

(c) The quantity of sweets sold at a shop in four days is given.

Day	Tuesday	Wednesday	Thursday	Friday
Quantity	362 kg	429 kg	217 kg	583 kg

Arrange the quantity sold in descending (decreasing) order.

```
┌─────────────────────────────────────────────────────────┐
│                                                         │
│                                                         │
└─────────────────────────────────────────────────────────┘
```

(d) The table gives the number of trees planted by different organizations in the past two months.

Organization	Heal the World	Go Green	Prakriti	Earthlings
Number of trees	684	648	468	486

Arrange the number of trees planted in ascending (increasing) order.

```
┌─────────────────────────────────────────────────────────┐
│                                                         │
│                                                         │
└─────────────────────────────────────────────────────────┘
```

> 📋 **Objective:** To skip count by 2, 10, and 100
>
> ⏳ **Time Required:** ~10 minutes
>
> ✏️ **Materials Required:** Abacus with disks/beads

Step 1: Form the number 362 on the abacus.

(a) Number of beads in the hundreds place = [   ]

(b) Number of beads in the tens place = [   ]

(c) Number of beads in the ones place = [   ]

Step 2: Let us skip count by 2. This can be done by adding 2 ones on the ones rod.

(a) Add 2 beads and write the number. [   ]

(b) Add 2 more and write the number. [   ]

(c) Add 2 more and write the number. [   ]

(d) Add 2 more. How many ones are there? [   ]

(e) If there are enough ones, replace ten ones with one ten and write the number. [   ]

(f) Add 2 beads in the ones rod and write the number. [   ]

Step 3: Let us now skip count by 10. This can be done by adding 1 tens bead to the tens rod.

Start with the number 372 on the abacus.

(a) Add 1 tens bead to the tens rod and write the number.

(b) Add another tens bead to the tens rod and write the number.

(c) Add one more tens bead. How many tens are there?

(d) If there are enough tens, replace 10 tens with one hundreds and write the number.

(e) Fill in the boxes.

| 402 | | | | | |

Step 4: Let us now skip count by 100.

(a) Form the number 322 on the abacus.

(b) Add one hundreds bead. Write the number.

(c) Add hundreds bead one by one and fill in the boxes.

| 422 | | | | | |

Date:

Status:

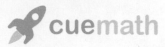

1 Skip count by 2 and box the numbers you reach.

(a)

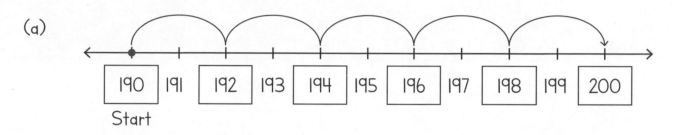

190 191 192 193 194 195 196 197 198 199 200
Start

(b)

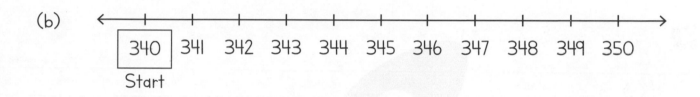

340 341 342 343 344 345 346 347 348 349 350
Start

(c)

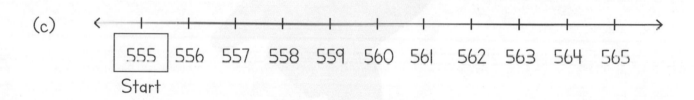

555 556 557 558 559 560 561 562 563 564 565
Start

2 Skip count by 3 and box the numbers you reach.

(a)

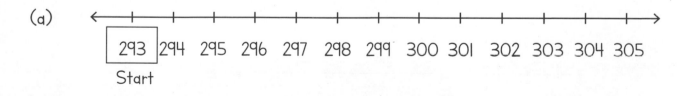

293 294 295 296 297 298 299 300 301 302 303 304 305
Start

(b)

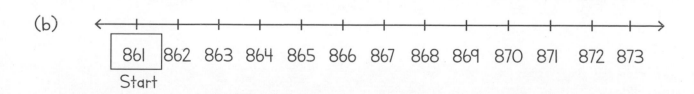

861 862 863 864 865 866 867 868 869 870 871 872 873
Start

3 Skip count by 2 and fill in the boxes.

(a)

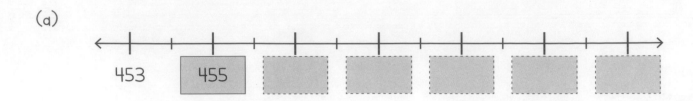

453   455

(b)

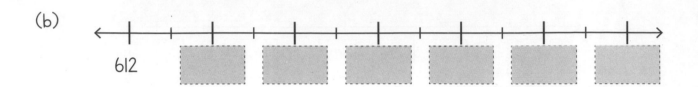

612

4 Skip count by 3 and fill in the boxes.

(a)

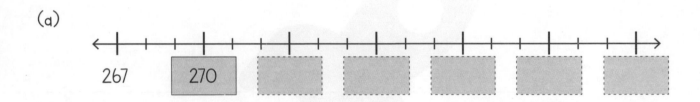

267   270

(b)

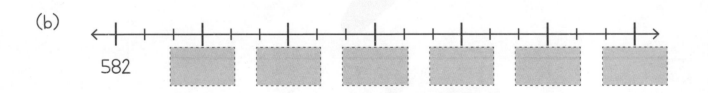

582

(c)

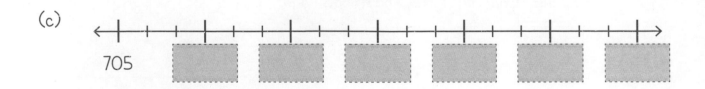

705

Date:

Status:

1 Skip count by 5 and fill in the boxes.

(a)

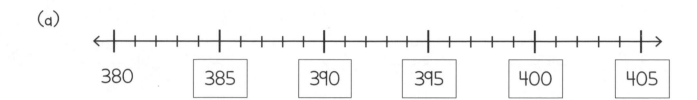

380 | 385 | 390 | 395 | 400 | 405

(b)

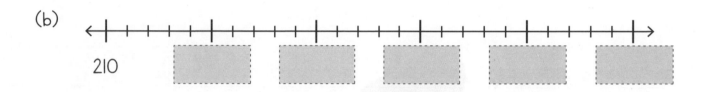

210

(c)

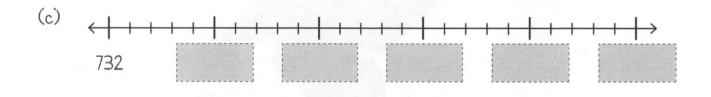

732

(d)

355

(e)

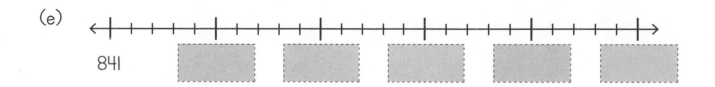

841

2 Skip count by 10 and fill in the boxes.

(a)

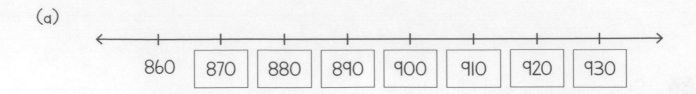

860 | 870 | 880 | 890 | 900 | 910 | 920 | 930

(b)

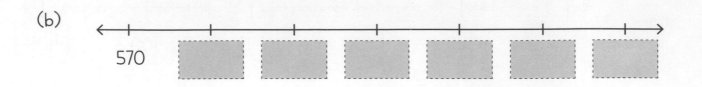

570

(c)

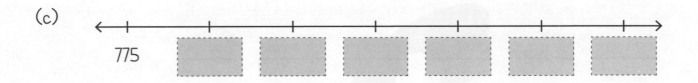

775

(d)

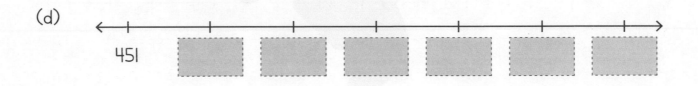

451

(e)

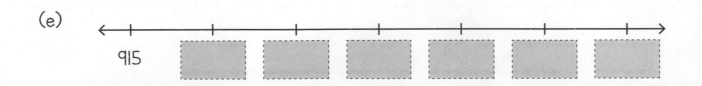

915

(f)

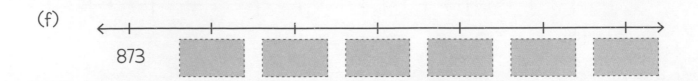

873

Date: [   ]   Status: [   ]

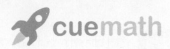

1 Skip count by 10 and fill in the boxes.

(a)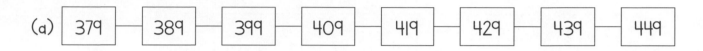

| 379 | 389 | 399 | 409 | 419 | 429 | 439 | 449 |

(b) | 758 | | | | | | |

(c) | 841 | | | | | | |

2 Skip count by 100 and fill in the boxes.

(a) | 0 | 100 | 200 | | | | | |

(b) | 310 | 410 | | | | | |

(c) | 258 | | | | | | |

(d) | 399 | | | | | | |

3 Identify the skip count and fill in the boxes. Tick (✓) the correct skip count.

(a) | 250 | 260 | 270 | 280 | 290 | 300 |

☐ 5
✓ 10
☐ 100

(b) | 600 | 602 | | | | |

☐ 2
☐ 5
☐ 100

(c) | 860 | 870 | | | | |

☐ 3
☐ 10
☐ 100

(d) | 211 | | | 511 | | |

☐ 5
☐ 10
☐ 100

(e) | | | | 640 | 660 | |

☐ 10
☐ 20
☐ 50

(f) | | | 750 | 800 | | |

☐ 10
☐ 50
☐ 100

1 Round off the number to the nearest ten. Tick (✓) the ten closest to it.

(a)

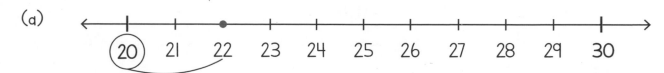

Which is the nearest ten to 22? 20 ✓ 30 ☐

22 rounded off to the nearest ten is 20 .

(b)

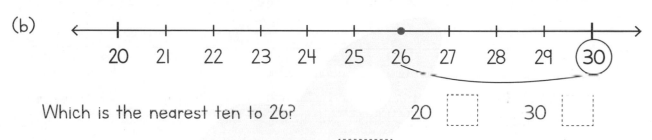

Which is the nearest ten to 26? 20 ☐ 30 ☐

26 rounded off to the nearest ten is ☐ .

(c)

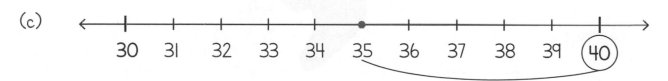

35 lies exactly between 30 and 40. In such cases, we round off the number to the higher ten.

(d)

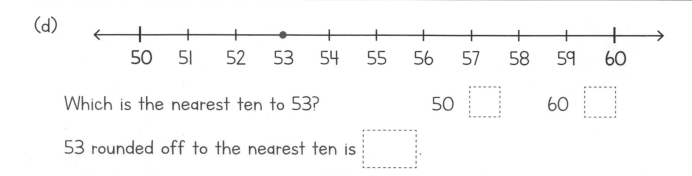

Which is the nearest ten to 53? 50 ☐ 60 ☐

53 rounded off to the nearest ten is ☐ .

Mark the given number on the number line, identify the tens closest to it, and round it off to the nearest ten.

(a) 68

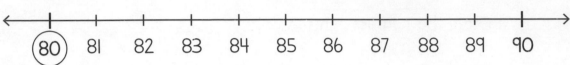

68 rounded off to the nearest ten is ⬚ 70 .

(b) 80

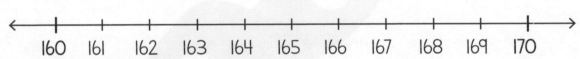

80 rounded off to the nearest ten is ⬚ 80 .

(c) 169

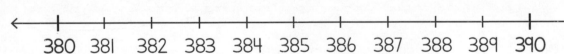

169 rounded off to the nearest ten is ⬚ .

(d) 383

383 rounded off to the nearest ten is ⬚ .

(e) 598

598 rounded off to the nearest ten is ⬚ .

Date: [ ]   Status: [ ]

cuemath

1 Mark the given number on the number line. Then identify the hundred closest to it and round it off to the nearest hundred.

(a) 140

(100) 110 120 130 140 150 160 170 180 190 200

140 rounded off to the nearest hundred is | 100 |.

(b) 180

100 110 120 130 140 150 160 170 180 190 200

180 rounded off to the nearest hundred is [ ].

(c) 250

200 210 220 230 240 250 260 270 280 290 300

250 lies exactly between 200 and 300. It is rounded off to | 300 |.

(d) 390

300 310 320 330 340 350 360 370 380 390 400

390 rounded off to the nearest hundred is [ ].

(e) 510

500 510 520 530 540 550 560 570 580 590 600

510 rounded off to the nearest hundred is [ ].

Approximately mark the number on the number line. Then, round it off to the nearest hundred.

(a) 325

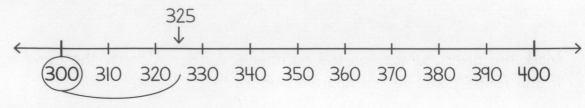

325 rounded off to the nearest hundred is ⬚.

(b) 483

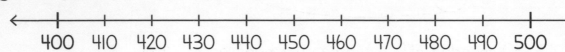

483 rounded off to the nearest hundred is ⬚.

(c) 658

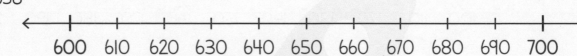

658 rounded off to the nearest hundred is ⬚.

(d) 820

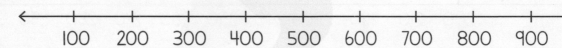

820 rounded off to the nearest hundred is ⬚.

(e) 595

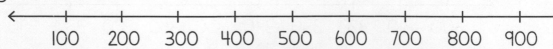

595 rounded off to the nearest hundred is ⬚.

(f) 931

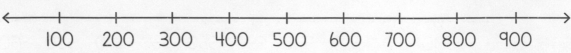

931 rounded off to the nearest hundred is ⬚.

Date:

Status:

cuemath

1 Round off each number to the nearest ten.

	Number	Rounded off to the nearest ten			Number	Rounded off to the nearest ten
(a)	446	450		(e)	925	930
(b)	865			(f)	58	
(c)	379			(g)	636	
(d)	912			(h)	842	

2 Round off each number to the nearest hundred.

	Number	Rounded off to the nearest hundred			Number	Rounded off to the nearest hundred
(a)	389	400		(e)	513	
(b)	800			(f)	220	
(c)	95			(g)	859	
(d)	722			(h)	601	

3 Answer the following questions.

(a) Sajan wanted to buy 187 candies for his birthday. Mark the number of candies he wanted to buy on the number line and round it off to the nearest ten.

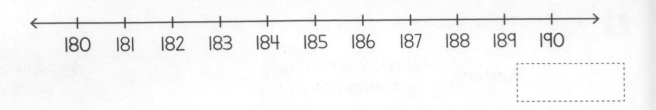

(b) A building has 805 people in it. Approximately mark the number of people on the number line and round it off to the nearest hundred.

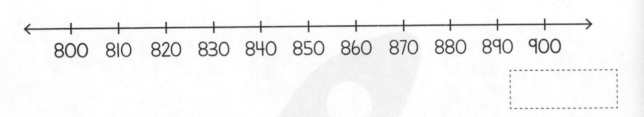

(c) Laya has ₹105. Approximately, how many hundreds does she have?

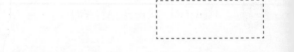

(d) Punya has 5 ten-rupee notes, 6 one-rupee coins, and 5 hundred-rupee notes. Round off the amount she has to the nearest hundred.

(e) There are 285 birds in a park. Round off the number of birds to the nearest ten.

(f) Kala teaches 150 students. Round off the number of students to the nearest hundred.

1 Answer the following questions.

(a) There are 6 seats in the first row, 10 in the second row, 14 in the third and so on. How many seats will be there in the sixth row?

6,   10,   14, . . .
      +4   +4   +4

Fourth row : 14 + 4 = 18
Fifth row   : 18 + 4 = 22
Sixth row   : 22 + 4 = 26

| 26 |

(b) Manny read four pages of a book on the first day, 7 on the second day, 10 on the third day and so on. If Manny took five days to read the complete book, how many pages were there in the book?

(c) John has 120 toffees. Every day, he gives away 10 toffees. How many days will it take for him to give away all the toffees?

(d) In a hall, there were 5 seats in the first row, 10 in the second, 15 in the third, 20 in the fourth and so on. How many seats will be there in the eighth row?

2 Answer the following questions.

(a) How many '1's are there in the numbers from 101 to 120?

(b) Form the smallest 3-digit number using only 4, 2, and 6.

Use the digits 1, 5, and 3, each of them exactly once to create a 3-digit number greater than the above number.

(c) What is the largest number which when rounded off to the nearest ten gives 380?

(d) Form all possible 3-digit numbers with the digits 7, 3, and 5, with no repeated digits.

Which among them is the greatest?

Which among them is the smallest?

(e) How many 3-digit numbers have exactly two 7s?

Date:

Status:

Cuemath Puzzle Time

1. How many 3-digit numbers have the same digit in the ones and the hundreds place?

2 In a game, there are 5 coins of ₹100, 5 coins of ₹10, and 5 coins of ₹1.

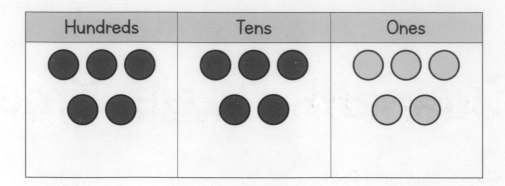

What are the maximum and the minimum money amounts that you can make if you choose only 6 coins (at least one of each type) out of 15?

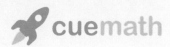

YAY!

I,_____, have successfully completed the module.

I have learnt to compare and order 3-digit numbers. I also know how to skip count and round off numbers.

I am curious to learn about odd, even, and ordinal numbers.

To the teacher : *You can now mark this module "complete" on the CueTeacher app. Doing this will activate the module assessment on the CueStudent app.*

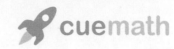

Date: [   ]   Status: [   ]

---

1 Compare the two numbers. Use >, <, or =.

(a) 123 [____] 346

(b) 290 [____] 271

(c) 352 [____] 359

(d) 620 [____] 260

(e) 785 [____] 391

(f) 249 [____] 942

---

2 Neha paid ₹232 for lunch and Rima paid ₹323 for lunch. Who paid more?

[_____]

---

3 Sara paid exactly 2 hundred-rupee notes and 1 ten-rupee note for an item while Mohan paid exactly 3 ten-rupee notes, 1 hundred-rupee note, and 5 one-rupee coins for an item. Who paid less?

[_____]

4 Write the three numbers and answer.

(a)

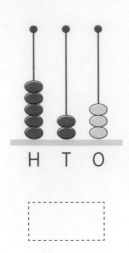 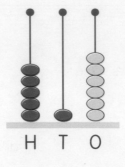 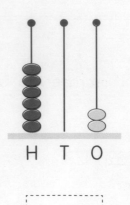

H T O   H T O   H T O

┌─────────┐   ┌─────────┐   ┌─────────┐
│   │   │   │   │   │
└─────────┘   └─────────┘   └─────────┘

The greatest number is ┌─────────┐ .

The smallest number is ┌─────────┐ .

5 Circle the greatest number.

(a)	584,	693,	311	(c)	293,	158,	239
(b)	765,	567,	657	(d)	812,	821,	828

6 Circle the smallest number.

(a)	455,	976,	155	(c)	317,	619,	371
(b)	845,	485,	584	(d)	767,	677,	776

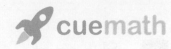

Date: [ ]   Status: [ ]

---

1 Answer the following.

(a) Make the smallest 3-digit number that has no ones and no zeros, without repeating any digit. [ ]

(b) Make the largest 3-digit number using any three digits out of 4, 6, 8, and 2, without repeating any of them. [ ]

(c) Make the smallest 3-digit number using 3, 2, and 7 without repeating any of them. [ ]

2 Order the numbers.

(a) A = 932, B = 387, C = 493, D = 893

[ ] > [ ] > [ ] > [ ]

(b) A = 568, B = 397, C = 586, D = 937

[ ] > [ ] > [ ] > [ ]

3 Skip count.

(a) | 260 | 270 | | | | | |

(b) | | | 535 | 635 | | | |

(c) | | | | | | 864 | 869 |

4 Do as directed.

(a)

40 41 42 43 44 45 46 47 48 49 50

43 rounded off to the nearest ten is ⬚.

(b)

0 100 200 300 400 500 600 700 800 900

563 rounded off to the nearest hundred is ⬚.

5 Make the largest possible 3-digit number using all the three digits given. Then round that number off to the nearest ten and the nearest hundred.

	Digits	Largest possible 3-digit number	Round off to nearest ten	Round off to nearest hundred
(a)	2, 5, 3			
(b)	8, 7, 1			
(c)	6, 2, 5			
(d)	7, 8, 0			